First edition 2016

Library of Congress Catalogue Number pending

ISBN 978-0-692-67871-8

RiMarcable Publications
PO BOX 20751
New York, NY 10023

visit us at www.rimarcablepublications.com

Theodore and Hazel
and the Bird

By
Riza Printup
and Marcus Printup

Illustrations by
Elyse Whittaker-Paek

The sun was shining brightly in the sky.
It was such a beautiful day.
So Theodore and Hazel, with trumpet and harp,
went to the park to play.

As they skipped along a path,
they came across a bird who looked so very sad.
Apparently the song he would always sing,
somehow he *no* longer had.

"I think I lost my song." said the Bird
as his tears began to flow.
"I open up my beak to sing
and I sound like this ... hhhhhhhhhho!"

"Oh *no!*" cried Theodore and Hazel
"Little Bird, what can we do?
Would it be all right if we help look around
and try to find the song for you?"

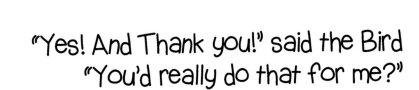

"Yes! And Thank you!" said the Bird
"You'd really do that for me?"

"Of course!" replied Theodore and Hazel
"Helping friends is totally our cup o' tea!"

Thank you!

So they walked and walked around the park,
looking through the grass and between the trees,
when suddenly they heard a peculiar sound,
down by their knees ...

"Is that the song I lost?
Oh could it be, possibly?"

"No Little Bird.
That's a DOG and her song.
We'll keep looking and find yours soon.
Don't you worry."

They continued to walk a little bit more,
when they heard ...

"Is that the song I lost?
Oh could it be, possibly?"

"No Little Bird. That's a BICYCLE BELL and its song. Let's *not* give up. Perseverance is the key."

And so again, they walked
just a little bit more before hearing ...

"Is that the song I lost?
Oh could it be, possibly?"

"No Little Bird.
That's an OPERA SINGER and his song.
And it sounds like he's practicing ...
we should let him be."

Then the Bird plopped himself down
as he started to give up.

"I don't know if I'll ever find my song.
I could cry all my tears into this cup!"

"Oh Little Bird, please don't cry!"
begged Theodore and Hazel
on their knees.

They reached out to hug the Bird,
when suddenly ...

He sneezed!!

He sneezed out TWO PEAS!!

TWO PEAS?

TWO PEAS?

TWO PEAS from his sneeze?

He started to get himself together
when they heard something familiar
from the trees ...

"Are ANY of these the song I lost?
Oh could it be, possibly?"

"Look Little Bird!
Those are BIRDS just like you.
So YES, it's very likely!"

Tweet

Tu

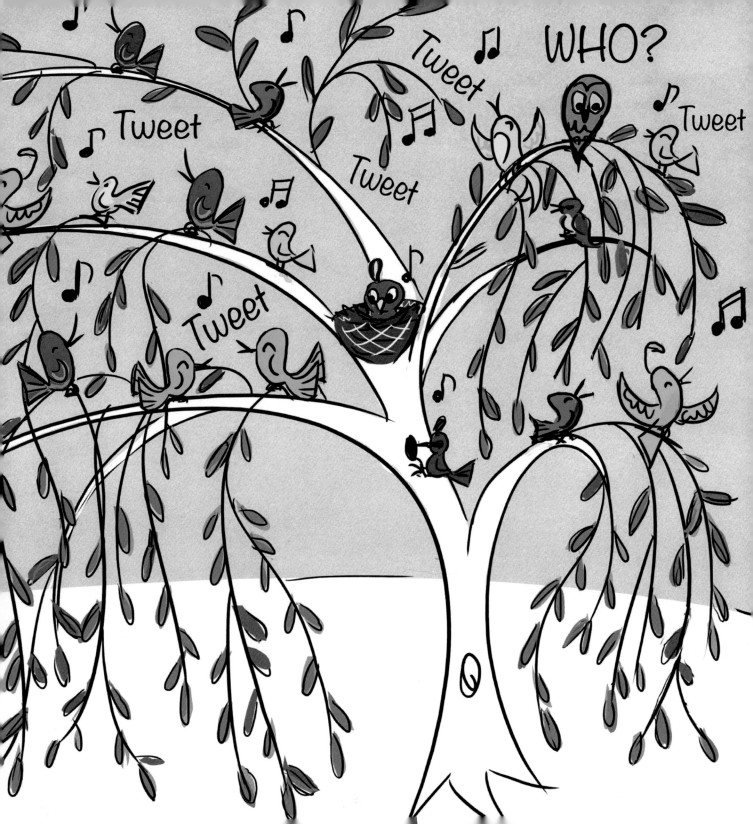

Then they asked the Bird to close his eyes
and take a breath, deep and long.

"Don't be afraid of what may come out.
As long as it's from YOUR HEART, make it big and strong."

So he took that breath,
fluttered his feathers and ...

The Bird found his song!!
As indeed he had had it all along.

Now, about those peas ...
The End?

THE BIRD'S SONG

Music and Lyrics
By Riza Printup

I have a song inside my heart
I've always had it right from the start
And when I listen carefully
It's beautiful because it's me

Sometimes my song is sad and kinda blue
It may be because my heart broke in two
But when my heart is full of joy and light
I want to share it with all
And with all of my might

I have a song inside my heart
I've always had it right from the start
And when I listen carefully
It's beautiful
It's amazing
Because it's me

You have a song inside your heart
You've always had it right from the start
And if you listen carefully
It's beautiful because it's meant to be

Sometimes the song is sad and kinda blue
It's maybe because your heart broke in two
But when your heart is full of joy and light
Don't you want to share it with all
And with all of your might?

We all have songs inside our hearts
We've always had them right from the start
And if we listen carefully
They're BEAUTIFUL
They're AMAZING
As they're meant to be!

WHO?

For

Annaliese, Trinity & Dylan
Jourdan, Cameron Jr, Cory,
Madonna & Emani

along with all of our
other amazing
nieces and nephews

May you always sing the
beautiful and powerful song
already in YOUR HEART

xoxo M & R

References
Cover Pages | Harlem Brownstones

Central Park, NYC
pp 1-4, 7-8 • Naumburg Bandshell, Manhattan Skyline
pp 11-12 • Cherry Blossom Trees
pp 15-16 • Jaqueline Kennedy Onassis Reservoir, Upper West Side Skyline
pp 19-20 • Bethesda Terrace (backside)
pp 21-22 • Bethesda Fountain

48379187R00023

Made in the USA
Middletown, DE
17 September 2017